JAZZ
ALTO SAX
LEVEL/GRADE 1
TUNES

ABRSM

Lead Jazz Consultant: Charles Beale
Sax Consultants: Iain Dixon, Mike Hall, Martin Hathaway, Andy Panayi,
   Tony Woods
Consultant Jazz Editors: Pete Churchill, Nikki Iles
Project Editor: Hywel Davies

Special thanks are also due to the following for their help in developing the
repertoire for this project:
John Barton, Mark Bassey, Chris Batchelor, Dave Bitelli, Jim Clarke, Dave Cliff,
Alan Cohen, Ralf Dorrell, Digby Fairweather, Sid Gauld, Frank Griffith, Stuart Hall,
Eddie Harvey, Paul Jayasinha, Mike Mower, Keith Nichols, Mark Nightingale,
Gerard Presencer, Brian Priestley, Simon Purcell, Geoff Simkins, Stan Sulzmann,
Ray Warleigh, Huw Warren, Steve Waterman, Annie Whitehead

Music setting by Barnes Music Engraving Ltd, East Sussex

designed by ●●● 9thplanet

Printed in England by Caligraving Ltd, Thetford, Norfolk

CONTENTS

Notice
ABRSM has reluctantly had to remove this piece from this book since, despite many efforts, we have been unable to obtain permission from the copyright owner to reproduce it for this reprint.

JAZZ ALTO SAX
LEVEL/GRADE 1
INTRODUCTION

Welcome to this book of jazz tunes, arranged for alto sax Level/Grade 1, which forms part of the ABRSM Jazz Syllabus. The tunes cover a wide range of styles – from gospel and swing through to funk and South African township – and are divided into three lists: Blues & Roots, Standards and Contemporary Jazz.

In each category there are five tunes. Each arrangement contains a fully notated HEAD, the main melody; an indication of the feel, that is straight 8s or swing; and a tempo indication (a metronome mark) representing the **minimum** exam speed for the tune at this Level/Grade. Every tune has at least one section for improvisation, marked SOLOS, with a simple chord sequence and set of guideline pitches. These pitches – appearing in boxes and shown as black noteheads without tails – give a suggested starting point to help you begin soloing. As you become more familiar with the material, you should experiment with using other pitches.

Blues & Roots draws from all periods of jazz and contains tunes based on the 12-bar blues or blues of other lengths. The list also includes African-American spirituals, other musics of New Orleans, and roots tunes from other continents. The tunes and chord sequences (or 'changes') in this list are mostly groove-based and are relatively straightforward.

Standards, as the term suggests, contains core repertoire of the jazz tradition. This includes familiar Tin Pan Alley and Broadway tunes, arranged in the rhythmic and harmonic styles of jazz, and more recent standards from swing, bebop, hard bop and other established styles. Some arrangements reproduce important past performances, while others give new perspectives on familiar tunes. Occasionally, lesser-known tunes by important performers or composers are also included. In this list, chord sequences and structures often incorporate AABA forms and II-V-I progressions.

Contemporary Jazz represents the vibrancy, eclecticism and even the fragmentation of jazz since the early 1970s. There are fusion pieces and overlaps with related styles, including rock and folk musics from around the world, plus contemporary tunes from South Africa, Europe and the American continent. Some tunes from this list were specially commissioned by ABRSM.

JAZZ ALTO SAX
LEVEL/GRADE 1
INTRODUCTION

Jazz is an aural tradition; the best way to learn is to listen to live or recorded performances. It is always good to hear how other performers have interpreted tunes you are working on, or to listen to tunes that are similar in style. With this in mind, each arrangement carries at least one Related Listening suggestion: a track, its album and record label. The availability of the listed albums has been checked as thoroughly as possible, but jazz recordings continually go in and out of issue. If you have difficulty finding them, try your local library (which usually has access to other libraries), the Internet or a specialist jazz-record supplier. In place of a specific label, 'various' indicates that the artist recorded this tune on a number of albums (including compilations) and that any of these recordings is considered suitable.

Additionally, for each arrangement, there is a footnote on the tune's history or style, its composer(s) or key performers, and, where relevant, technical advice from a jazz saxophonist. We hope that these insights provide fresh ideas and will help you develop a sense of style.

The CD at the back of this book contains a recording of each arrangement and a 'minus-one' version of the track for you to play along with. The minus-one tracks can be used in ABRSM jazz exams (we accept, however, that live accompaniment – whether small band or piano, guitar etc. – is truer to the spirit of jazz). The recorded arrangement reflects the exam routine; please note the number of bars required for the exam solo. Outside the exam – while practising or in non-exam performances – you can extend solos by repeating all or part of the SOLOS section.

At Levels/Grades 1–3 some of the tunes are arranged in keys other than the original, so that they are playable by less experienced musicians. By Level/Grade 4, however, all tunes are in their most regularly performed keys.

Jazz exams offer a great way to measure your progress, to give your work an added focus and to enable you to achieve your potential. ABRSM's graded exams are based on what an average student achieves during the course of one year, so that Level/Grade 5, for example, represents five years' work. At every level, candidates for these exams are assessed by musicians with broad jazz experience. For more information, please read 'Playing the Tunes in an Exam' at the back of this book.

We hope you enjoy playing these tunes as much as we have enjoyed selecting, arranging and recording them.

LAS VEGAS TANGO

GIL EVANS
arr. Pete Saberton

SONNYMOON FOR TWO

SONNY ROLLINS
arr. Richard Michael

> **Notice**
> ABRSM has reluctantly had to remove this piece from this book since, despite many efforts, we have been unable to obtain permission from the copyright owner to reproduce it for this reprint.

SONNYMOON FOR TWO

SONNY ROLLINS
arr. Richard Michael

NOBODY KNOWS THE TROUBLE I'VE SEEN

TRADITIONAL
arr. Liam Noble

This traditional African-American gospel tune has a strong blues feeling. Bassist Charlie Haden (b. 1937), in the recommended listening, worked with Ornette Coleman in the 1950s and 60s, playing what became known as 'free jazz'. On *Steal Away* Haden and pianist Hank Jones return to a more traditional style.

RELATED LISTENING Charlie Haden and Hank Jones: 'Nobody Knows the Trouble I've Seen' from *Steal Away* (Verve)

SHORT STOP

SHORTY ROGERS
arr. Malcolm Miles

American trumpeter and arranger Shorty Rogers (1924–94) was a leading figure of the West Coast style of the 1950s. 'Short Stop' is a riff blues: a short, punchy rhythmic figure is repeated over a blues chord-sequence.
RELATED LISTENING Shorty Rogers: 'Short Stop' from *Short Stops* (RCA Victor)
Count Basie: 'Jumpin' at the Woodside' (various)

FREDDIE FREELOADER

MILES DAVIS
arr. Pete Churchill

This is a blues from the 1959 album *Kind of Blue* by Miles Davis (1926–91). After all the fury and complexity of bebop, Miles wanted to play simpler tunes with fewer chords and more space, to develop a more personal expression.

RELATED LISTENING Miles Davis: 'Freddie Freeloader' from *Kind of Blue* (Columbia/Sony)

SOLITUDE

DUKE ELLINGTON, EDDIE DELANGE & IRVING MILLS
arr. Steve Hill

Duke Ellington (1899–1974) is one of the most celebrated composers in jazz. His approach included writing compositions that suited the sound and improvising style of individual members of his bands.
RELATED LISTENING Duke Ellington and Coleman Hawkins: 'Solitude' from *Duke Ellington Meets Coleman Hawkins* (Impulse!)

SOMBRERO SAM

CHARLES LLOYD
arr. Liam Noble & Will Michael

During the 1960s, tenor (and sometimes alto) sax player Charles Lloyd (b. 1938) brought elements of 'free jazz' to rock audiences. A 'sombrero' is a wide-brimmed Mexican straw hat.
RELATED LISTENING Charles Lloyd: 'Sombrero Sam' (various)
Charles Lloyd: *Journey Within/In Europe* (Collectables)

IDAHO

JESSE STONE
arr. Pete Churchill

'Idaho' became a jazz standard in the 1940s, after being recorded by Benny Goodman and Les Hite. In the hands of Count Basie, this tune is both fast and rhythmic. Notice how well the melody swings against the driving pulse of the bass line.
RELATED LISTENING The Art Tatum, Benny Carter, Louis Bellson Trio: 'Idaho' from *The Tatum Group Masterpieces*, vol. 1 (Pablo)
Benny Carter: 'Idaho' from *A Gentleman and his Music* (Concord Jazz)
Count Basie: 'Idaho' from *Ain't Misbehavin'* (Laserlight)

14 Music and lyrics by Jesse Stone

IS YOU IS, OR IS YOU AIN'T (MA' BABY)?

BILLY AUSTIN & LOUIS JORDAN
arr. Pete Churchill

Saxophonist Louis Jordan (1908–75) and his group Tympany Five played rhythm-and-blues, a precursor of rock-and-roll. 'Is you is' is a favourite with singers. Listen for that catchy lick in the accompaniment, after the first phrase.
RELATED LISTENING Louis Jordan: 'Is you is, or Is you ain't (ma' Baby)?' (various)

MACK THE KNIFE

KURT WEILL & BERTOLT BRECHT
arr. Dave Bitelli & Nikki Iles

'Mack the Knife' was made a jazz standard by Louis Armstrong and Ella Fitzgerald, and comes from Kurt Weill's *The Threepenny Opera* (1928). It is often played modulating a semitone higher every 16 or 32 bars.
RELATED LISTENING Sonny Rollins: 'Moritat' from *Saxophone Colossus* (Prestige)
Ben Webster: 'Mack the Knife' from *Stormy Weather* (Black Lion)
Kenny Garrett: 'Mack the Knife' from *African Exchange Student* (Atlantic)

JEAN PIERRE

MILES DAVIS
arr. Charles Beale

Straight 8s ♩ = 82 **Childlike but groovy**

MO' BETTER BLUES

BILL LEE
arr. Bill Kinghorn

Straight 8s ♩ = 92 **Laid back**

Jazz bassist Bill Lee (b. 1928) wrote the scores for several films by Spike Lee, the composer's filmmaker son. This tune is from Spike's 1990 film of the same title and its soundtrack featuring Branford Marsalis, the tenor and soprano saxophonist.
RELATED LISTENING Branford Marsalis Quartet, with Terence Blanchard: *Mo' Better Blues* (Columbia)

MANNENBERG

ABDULLAH IBRAHIM
arr. Huw Warren

Slow township groove ♩ = 76

Abdullah Ibrahim (b. 1934), formerly known as Dollar Brand, is a celebrated South African pianist. This tune contains the characteristic 'three-chord trick' used in much South African jazz. As in the blues, while the underlying harmony is quite simple, the melody and rhythm provide variety over the repeating groove and create music of great emotional depth.
RELATED LISTENING Abdullah Ibrahim: 'Mannenberg' from *The Mountain* (Camden)

EVERYTHING THAT LIVES LAMENTS

KEITH JARRETT
arr. Charles Beale

OYE COMO VA

TITO PUENTE
arr. Charles Beale

This is a popular tune in 'salsa' – dance music, with elements of jazz, originally played by Cuban and Puerto Rican musicians living in New York. Try clapping and practising the *clave* (pronounced cla-veh) rhythm of the accompaniment from bars 1–4.
RELATED LISTENING Tito Puente: 'Oye como va' (various)
Santana: 'Oye como va' from *Abraxas* (CBS/Sony)

Music and lyrics by Tito Puente
© Copyright 1963, 1970 (Renewed 1991, 1998) EMI FULL KEEL MUSIC.
This arrangement © 2003 EMI FULL KEEL MUSIC. EMI Music Publishing (WP) Ltd, 127 Charing Cross Road, London WC2 0QY. Used by permission of Music Sales Ltd, EMI Music Publishing Ltd, EMI Music Publishing Australia Pty Ltd, Fujipacific Music (S.E. Asia) Ltd and Hal Leonard Corp.

PLAYING THE TUNES IN AN EXAM

In the exam you are required to perform three tunes from this book, one from each list. You will also have to do a number of supporting tests, which measure your technical proficiency, musicianship and ability to improvise. For full details of the exam, please refer to the Jazz Syllabus, which is available free of charge from music retailers, our website (www.abrsm.org) or from ABRSM, 24 Portland Place, London W1B 1LU, United Kingdom.

PREPARING THE TUNES

Jazz is an aural tradition, and we expect that you will learn the tunes from the CD as well as from the printed music. For the exam, the tunes do not have to be played exactly as written, and in fact embellishment of the HEAD (as distinct from improvisation in the SOLOS section) is expected, particularly after the SOLOS section.

In the exam the following elements of the given material must be in place:

- *the correct feel* – 'straight 8s' or 'swing', as and where marked.

- *the minimum speed.* The tempo marking, representing the minimum speed, should be observed in order to demonstrate the technical control required at the Level/Grade. You may prefer to play the tune faster and this is equally acceptable.

- *the melody of the HEAD.* This may be embellished – indeed, examiners will expect some embellishment on the return of the HEAD – but it must be recognizable. Your interpretation should demonstrate an understanding of the HEAD's main musical elements, such as important kicks, other rhythmic figures and the melody's contours, and of the musical character of the arrangement.

- *the routine*, that is the form of the arrangement, with the intro (where applicable), HEAD and SOLOS containing the correct number of bars. The length of solo for the exam is indicated at the end of SOLOS, in both score and part. (Many tunes contain repeat signs around the SOLOS section, to enable you to play longer solos in non-exam performances.)

- *the improvisation.* In Level/ Grade 1–3 exams the rhythmic and melodic aspects of your improvisation (in the SOLOS section) are assessed. At these early stages we expect your understanding of the relationship between melody and harmony to be developing gradually, as part of your playing, but this will not be assessed in the exam. Taking some account of the harmonic context in your solo will be given credit at Level/Grade 4 Distinction and above.

EMBELLISHING AND IMPROVISING

The process of interpreting and personalizing the tune begins once the given material is secure.

Playing the HEAD

On the first playing, the notation of the HEAD should be closely followed. While there may be variation in details of melody, rhythm or phrasing, the result should be coherent, stylish and musical, and not alter the technical level. The amount and nature of embellishment will vary from tune to tune, depending on its style and musical character.

Occasionally the HEAD contains melody notes printed in small type, accompanied by the abbreviation 'opt.' (optional). This means either that there are two commonly known versions of the tune or that it has been necessary to alter the melody slightly to suit the Level/Grade. Playing these optional notes is not a requirement of the exam, nor will they be assessed as if part of the written HEAD. However, if you prefer to include these small-type notes in the exam, you may, particularly where they form part of an embellishment.

Soloing and using guideline pitches

The guideline pitches provide a starting point for your solo. They reflect the number and range of pitches an examiner might expect to hear, and they take account of the scale requirements of the Level/Grade.

Please note that while you may use the pitches as a foundation for your solo, you will not be assessed in the exam on whether or not the guideline pitches are actually used. You will be expected to expand upon the given material as your experience allows. As your playing develops, the chords will increasingly influence the pitches you choose.

Preparing to improvise

Aim at improvising your solos and embellishing the given material at the moment of performance. Pre-prepared solos often lack the freshness, spontaneity and spirit of risk-taking that are at the heart of jazz. However, you are strongly advised to get to know the chord sequences and grooves of the tunes you have selected, and to learn as many ways through them as possible. You will then be able to demonstrate your skills in the exam through varying the musical material.

After the solo

The SOLOS section is usually followed by 'HEAD continues': the section in which the opening melody returns. Everything here may be embellished in any number of ways, from a few simple additions or variations to a more extensive reworking. As a guide, embellishment at Level/Grade 1 can mean small changes to the rhythm or melody, or variation in dynamics and phrasing. At Level/Grade 3, players might transpose material at the octave, or introduce fills. Finally, by Level/Grade 5, melodic lines may be developed with greater intricacy, and rhythms

and phrasing reinterpreted. In short, exact repetition of earlier material should be avoided.

The performances on the CD demonstrate this approach, providing good examples of improvisations and embellishments of the given material. However, be inventive! Remember that examiners will be familiar with the CD and will notice slavish copying.

ACCOMPANIMENT

All the tunes must be played with an accompaniment. The options are:

- *minus-one backing-tracks*. The CD with this book includes a rhythm-section backing-track for each tune. In the exam these tracks are to be played on a portable CD player provided by the candidate. A tuning note is included on the CD.

- *written-out and improvised accompaniments*. Pianists may play from the fully written-out scores supplied with this book. Alternatively, the accompaniment may be improvised by a pianist, guitarist or other chordal accompanist, based on the written-out score, its chord symbols or a combination of the two.

- *small-band accompaniment*. Candidates may use a small band, provided the chord symbols and routines in this book are followed.

For further details, please refer to the Jazz Syllabus.

CD TRACK LISTING

TUNES

Performance/Minus-one

Blues & Roots

1	17	**LAS VEGAS TANGO** Gil Evans arr. Pete Saberton (*Warner Chappell Overseas Holdings Ltd*)
2	18	**SONNYMOON FOR TWO** Sonny Rollins arr. Richard Michael (*Sony/ATV Music Publishing (UK) Ltd*)
3	19	**NOBODY KNOWS THE TROUBLE I'VE SEEN** Traditional arr. Liam Noble (*Trad./ABRSM*)
4	20	**SHORT STOP** Shorty Rogers arr. Malcolm Miles (*Michele Publishing Co.*)
5	21	**FREDDIE FREELOADER** Miles Davis arr. Pete Churchill (*Sony/ATV Music Publishing (UK) Ltd*)

Standards

6	22	**SOLITUDE** Duke Ellington, Eddie DeLange & Irving Mills arr. Steve Hill (*Lafleur Music Ltd/ MCPS Reversionary Rights*)
7	23	**SOMBRERO SAM** Charles Lloyd arr. Liam Noble & Will Michael (*MCS Music Ltd*)
8	24	**IDAHO** Jesse Stone arr. Pete Churchill (*Famous Music Publishing Ltd*)
9	25	**IS YOU IS, OR IS YOU AIN'T (MA' BABY)?** Billy Austin & Louis Jordan arr. Pete Churchill (*Universal/MCA Music Ltd*)
10	26	**MACK THE KNIFE** Kurt Weill & Bertolt Brecht arr. Dave Bitelli & Nikki Iles (*GEMA/Universal Edition A.G. (Wien)/Universal Edition (London) Ltd*)

Contemporary Jazz

11	27	**JEAN PIERRE** Miles Davis arr. Charles Beale (*Sony/ATV Music Publishing (UK) Ltd*)
12	28	**MO' BETTER BLUES** Bill Lee arr. Bill Kinghorn (*Warner/Chappell North America Ltd*)
13	29	**MANNENBERG** Abdullah Ibrahim arr. Huw Warren (*enja European New Jazz Musik GmbH*)
14	30	**EVERYTHING THAT LIVES LAMENTS** Keith Jarrett arr. Charles Beale (*Kundalini Music Co.*)
15	31	**OYE COMO VA** Tito Puente arr. Charles Beale (*EMI Music Publishing (WP) Ltd*)
16		**TUNING NOTE** concert B♭

AURAL TESTS

32	**Test A, No. 1**
33	**Test B, No. 1**
34	**Test C, No. 2**

QUICK STUDIES

35	**No. 2** by ear
36	**No. 2** at sight

SCALES

37	**Mixolydian on D, 1 octave** swing
38	**C major, to a fifth** straight 8s
39	**Minor pentatonic on A, 1 octave** swing
40	**D minor arpeggio, 1 octave** straight 8s

Saxes: Alan Barnes, Steve Buckley, Iain Dixon, Tim Garland, Martin Hathaway, Mark Lockheart, Jamie O'Donnell, Andy Panayi, Stan Sulzmann, Rob Townsend

Keyboards: Robin Aspland, Pete Churchill, Nikki Iles, Liam Noble, Huw Warren, Jim Watson, Gareth Williams

Bass: Jeremy Brown, Orlando Le Fleming, Matt Miles, Dudley Phillips, Steve Watts

Drums/Percussion: Paul Clarvis, Mark Fletcher, Martin France, Nic France, Sebastiaan de Krom, Tristan Mailliot, Bosco de Oliveira, Clark Tracey

Accordion: Huw Warren **Guitar:** John Parricelli

Examiners: Charles Beale, Nikki Iles **Exam 'Candidates':** John Hayward, Nathan Hayward, Stan Sulzmann

Producers: Chris Batchelor, Charles Beale, Hywel Davies, Nikki Iles

Recording Engineer: Ken Blair

Assistant Recording Engineers: Jeremy Gill (Roundhouse), Gavin Goldberg (Metropolis), James Shannon (Surrey)

Recorded at The Roundhouse Studios, London, 25 March to 17 April and 24 June to 13 July 2002, Metropolis Studios Limited, London, 8 and 9 November 2002, and University of Surrey Studios, Guildford, 6 January 2003

A bmp production for ABRSM (Publishing) Ltd, a wholly owned subsidiary of ABRSM